BEN

D0588385

EGMONT

We bring stories to life

First published in Great Britain 2009
by Egmont UK Limited
239 Kensington High Street
London W8 6SA

Originally published in Indonesia in 2008 by Komik Warna.

Ben 10 and all related characters and elements
are trademarks of and © Cartoon Network.
(s09)

ISBN 978 1 4052 4664 4
3 5 7 9 10 8 6 4 2

Printed in Italy

BEN 10

CREATED BY
DUNCAN ROULEAU, JOE CASEY,
JOE KELLY AND STEVEN T. SEAGLE

WILDMUTT

GHOSTFREAK

HEATBLAST

BEN
TENNYSON

DIAMONDHEAD

VOLUME 2

WASHINGTON B.C.

WRITTEN BY
GREG KLEIN & THOMAS PUGSLEY

RIBBIT

RIBBIT

HUH?

HMM!

WHAT'S THIS? YOU'RE A CLOWN, TOO? HA-HA-HA!

THIS SPECIAL HELMET IS MY *TRANSMODULATOR*.

IT CREATES AND ACCELERATES MUTATION AT THE GENETIC LEVEL.

HEH, HEH!

DR. ANIMO'S HELMET FIRES A BLAST OF LIGHT AT THE FROG!

WATCH THIS!

HUH?

THE LASER SLOWLY INCREASES THE SIZE OF THE FROG UNTIL IT GROWS TO A GINORMOUS SIZE!

WHAA!

CROAK

CROAK

SLURRRPP!

SORRY, I CAN'T HEAR YOU. IT SOUNDS LIKE YOU HAVE A FROG IN YOUR THROAT . . . OR IS THAT THE OTHER WAY ROUND? HAHAHAHA!

PLUUGGH!

HAVING SWALLOWED THE LANDLORD, THE GIGANTIC FROG THEN SPITS HIM OUT!

EUGGH!

SQUELSH!

THWAPP!

DR. ANIMO CHARGES THROUGH THE WALL OF THE SUPERMARKET ON HIS GIGANTIC FROG.

HMM . . .

PERFECT, THE ELECTRONICS DEPARTMENT.

THIS IS JUST WHAT I NEED.

HEY, WHAT DO YOU THINK YOU'RE DOING?

47

OOWW!

BEEP! BEEP!

HMM!

WAIT! I DON'T NEED TO TURN INTO AN ALIEN TO STOP THIS OVERGROWN FURBALL!

BEN THROWS A BALL AT THE GIGANTIC HAMSTER'S HEAD, DISTRACTING IT FROM GWEN AND GRANDPA MAX.

THWACK!

GGRRR!

ROOAAR!

THUMP!

BEN SPEEDS AWAY ON A MOTOR-SCOOTER WITH THE HAMSTER CLOSE BEHIND.

VRROOM!

GRRRR!

UH . . . A DARN GOOD ONE! UH, BEN, WHAT'S THE MATTER?

I SAVED THE ENTIRE MEGA-MART FROM THAT MONSTER AND WHAT DO I GET FOR IT? NOTHING! IT ISN'T FAIR.

BEING A HERO DOESN'T MEAN THAT OTHER PEOPLE NEED TO KNOW YOU DID SOMETHING GOOD. IT MEANS YOU KNOW THAT *YOU* DID SOMETHING GOOD. BEING A HERO IS ITS OWN REWARD.

WHAT? WERE YOU READING THE GREETING CARDS AT THE MEGA-MART?

ACTUALLY . . . YES.

55

BUT HE WAS MUTATING ANIMALS IN ALL OF HIS EXPERIMENTS.

FIVE YEARS AGO, DR. ANIMO WAS A PROMISING VETERINARY SCIENTIST.

BINGO!

WHEN HE DIDN'T WIN SOME BIG PRIZE CALLED THE 'VERITIES AWARD', HE FLIPPED OUT.

ANYTHING ABOUT THAT SOUND FAMILIAR, BEN?

WE'VE LOST TRACK OF HIM! HE COULD BE GOING ANYWHERE IN WASHINGTON D.C.

OR WASHINGTON B.C.

THAT'S IT! I KNOW WHERE HE'S GOING! TO THE MUSEUM . . .

YOU ARE VERY PERSISTENT. I HATE PERSISTENT PEOPLE.

WE KNOW ALL ABOUT YOU AND YOUR WEIRD EXPERIMENTS, DR. ANIMO. IT'S OVER!

OH NO, IT'S ONLY JUST BEGINNING. I'VE FINISHED THE SECOND PHASE OF MY WORK, THE RE-ACTIVATION OF DORMANT CELLS.

UH . . . I DIDN'T UNDERSTAND ANY OF THAT. DID ANYONE GET WHAT HE WAS MUMBLING ABOUT?

IN OTHER WORDS, BRINGING BACK SOMETHING THAT HAS LONG BEEN DEAD.

OBSERVE!

CLICK!

ZAP!

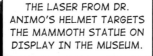

THE LASER FROM DR. ANIMO'S HELMET TARGETS THE MAMMOTH STATUE ON DISPLAY IN THE MUSEUM.

WHAT?

HUH?

BEHOLD THE GENIUS THAT IS DR. ANIMO!

WOAH!

THE MAMMOTH COMES TO LIFE.

NOW WOULD BE THE RIGHT TIME TO BE A HERO!

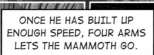

ONCE HE HAS BUILT UP
ENOUGH SPEED, FOUR ARMS
LETS THE MAMMOTH GO.

GRRR!

WHOOSH!

FOUR ARMS FLINGS THE
MAMMOTH INTO A PILLAR
AND THE MAMMOTH IS
BURIED BENEATH THE RUBBLE.

KABLAM!

OH, I THINK I'M
GONNA BE SICK!

WHY YOU . . .

I WOULD LIKE TO STAY LONGER . . .

BUT I HAVE TO GO AND GET WHAT I DESERVE.

DR. ANIMO RIDES THE T-REX OUT OF THE MUSEUM . . .

SMASH!

. . . FOLLOWED BY HIS PARROT.

THE PARROT SUDDENLY GRABS GWEN BY THE ARMS.

AAHH!

THE WATCH
ACTIVATES.

ZING!

THE ALIEN POWER
RUSHES THROUGH
BEN'S BODY!

ZAP!

ZAAPP!

FOUR MORE EYES APPEAR
ALONG BEN'S FACE.

WINGS GROW ON HIS BACK
AND LEGS SPROUT OUT OF
HIS SIDES.

KAPOW!

THE POWER OF THE WATCH
HAS TRANSFORMED HIM
INTO *STINKFLY*.

STINKFLY LIFTS HER INTO THE AIR AND BEGINS TO DIVE.

WHOOSH!

WOAH!

THEN HE THROWS HER INTO THE ARMS OF GRANDPA MAX.

I'VE GOT YOU!

LOOK OUT!

THUD!

HUH?

AAH!

BEHIND YOU!

CAAWW!

KAPOW!

82

THE LASER RADIATES OUTSIDE OF THE BUILDING.

ZZING!

CAAAW!

UH OH!

THE LASER STRIKES THE PARROT.

UHHHH!

ZAP!

ZZZAP!

IT TURNS THE PARROT BACK TO A NORMAL SIZE.

WHAT . . .

DON'T EVEN TRY TO KISS UP TO ME NOW!

NAME: HEATBLAST

ALIEN BACKGROUND:
HEATBLAST IS A PYRONITE,
WHO DESCENDS FROM THE
PYROS STAR. PYROS IS
SO HOT, IT FUNCTIONS
AS A SUN

SUPER POWER: HE CAN CREATE
FIRE IN ANY FORM, FROM FIRE BOMBS
TO FIRE ROCKETS. HIS FIRE
POWER IS UNLIMITED!

PHYSICAL FACT: HIS BODY
TEMPERATURE IS
EXTREMELY HIGH
AND HE CANNOT
LOWER IT TO A
HUMAN LEVEL

INTERESTING FACT: HE CAN CREATE
A HEAT VORTEX SO HE CAN CARRY PEOPLE
WITHOUT BURNING THEM

WEAKNESS: HUGE AMOUNTS OF SAND, WATER
OR FOAM COULD BE FATAL

HEATBLAST

BEN 10

EVER WISHED THE SCHOOL HOLIDAYS COULD BE MORE INTERESTING?

WIN A £20 EGMONT BOOK VOUCHER EVERY MONTH!

WIN!

Simply go to
WWW.EGMONT.CO.UK/COMPETITION
and tell us which adventures
you would like to go on!